This book belongs to:

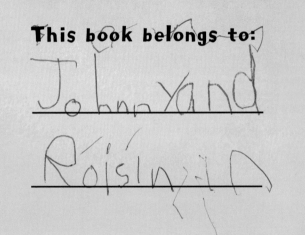

Johnyand

Roisin-D

This book is designed to encourage small children to talk about what they see in the colourful pictures. Some simple questions have been suggested, but many more can be made up.

Always try to find a quiet space to share this book with your child. Children will be generous with their responses if you encourage them and give them confidence. They so quickly learn new words and love to use them. A good vocabulary helps them to think and enables them to express their thoughts.

Most importantly, enjoy the book together.

Written by Kath Jewitt
Illustrated by Claire Henley
Language consultant: Betty Root

This edition published by Parragon in 2009

Parragon
Queen Street House
4 Queen Street
Bath BA1 1HE, UK

ISBN 978-1-4075-6805-8

Printed in China

My First Book of...

DIGGERS
and
DUMPERS

PaRRagon

Bath New York Singapore Hong Kong Cologne Delhi Melbourne

There are lots of machines on this building site.

Point to all
the different ones.

Do you know what these machines are called?

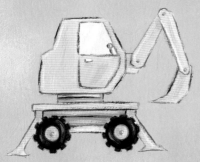

digger

dumper truck

rock breaker

steamroller

Point to each one and say its name.

bulldozer   cement mixer

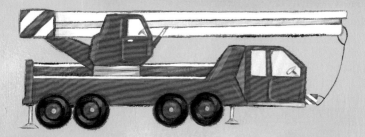

crane

This digger is working hard on the building site.

What is it doing?

Here is a dumper truck
with a heavy load.

What is happening
in this picture?

The bulldozer is moving
some heavy rocks.

Find another bulldozer in the picture.

This machine is called
a rock breaker.
It has a special arm.

The rock breaker uses its arm to break big rocks into small ones.

Point to the small rocks.

A cement mixer
mixes up cement.

What do you think these men are doing?

This crane has a long arm
to lift heavy things.

What is happening in this picture?

This machine uses its heavy roller to flatten the ground.

Can you remember what it is called?

People drive the machines
on the building site.

Point to the drivers in this picture.

What are the other workers doing?

The digger is yellow.
The bulldozer is green.

Find the red and blue machines in this picture.

What are all the machines doing?

Which one would you like to ride in?